SHINE-A-LIGHT
PRESS

Published in the United States of America by Shine-A-Light Press.
All rights reserved, including the right of reproduction in whole or in part in any form.
No part of this book may be reproduced in any form or by any electronic or mechanical means including
information storage and retrieval systems-except in the case of brief quotations embodied in critical articles
or reviews-or transmitted in any form or by any means electronic, mechanical, photocopying, recording,
or otherwise without permission in writing from its publisher.
For permissions, pleae email Shine-A-Light Press at info@ShineALightCorp.com.
Shine-A-Light Press and related logo are registered trademarks of Shine-A-Light, Corp.

Copyright ©2021, Ben Cooper
Book edit, layout and design by Andrea and Chris Elston

Educators and librarians, for a variety of teaching tools to use with this book,
visit us at www.shinealightpress.com

First paperback edition published by Shine-A-Light Press and printed in October 2021

Summary:
The unique attributes of a selection of furry creatures are beautifully portrayed in both verse and illustration
giving credit to the Master Creator for His wonderous works.

Library of Congress Control Number: 2021947294

ISBN: 978-1-953158-88-8

ISBN 978-1-953158-88-8

50899

9 781953 158888

Printed in the U.S.A. $8.99

Created Critters with Fur

Written by
Ben Cooper

SHINE-A-LIGHT
PRESS

Illustrated by
Sandy Arnold

This book is dedicated to my wife, Sonia, who homeschooled all five of our children
(Wesley, Haydn, Sean, Grace, and Suzanna).
Your tireless love and teaching skills are evident in the adults they have become.
Thank you for the labor of love you have invested into them.

Hidden Mouse Search

With a current estimate of 20 billion mice on the earth, they are by far the most common mammal. Mice can live in all kinds of climates and are found in nearly every country. The average female mouse will have nine litters per year and have anywhere from three to fourteen pups per litter. That means that an adult female mouse can give birth to over fifty mice each year. It is no wonder they hold the record for the highest population of mammals.

Why so many? Mice are at the bottom of the food chain. Many predators like owls, foxes, and coyotes rely on them as a major food source. Mice must be very prolific because of the hunting pressure from predators. Since their reproductive numbers are so high and they can live almost anywhere, they are said to be the most likely species to survive a worldwide, catastrophic event.

Now that you know how common the mouse is throughout the world, our illustrator has tucked away hidden images of a mouse in the pictures. Can you find them all?

Bear

Mama bear teaches her cubs how to STRIVE,

to learn how to hunt and ways to survive.

She shows where to find the best foods to eat,

by digging for grubs or fishing for meat.

Good training is given to **kids** as they grow,

to help them remember the things they should know.

"Train up a child in the way he should go;
even when he is old he will not depart from it."
Proverbs 22:6 6:26 (ESV)

Cattle

Cattle graze in pastures and w a n d e r about.

It's hard to restrain them, they keep getting out.

Farmers build |F|E|N|C|E|S| to keep them inside,

to provide for them boundaries to safely abide.

People will roam and will w a n d e r off too.

The Bible gives guidance to help them stay true.

"I have hidden your word in my heart
that I might not sin against you."
Psalm 119:11 (NIV)

Deer

All fawns are born with WHITE spots on RED,

the males grow up and get horns on their head.

His antlers turn into a *beautiful* crown,

and last but a season before falling *down*.

Of all the crowns that we have amassed,

only the things done for Jesus will last.

"...the twenty-four elders fall down before him who is seated on the throne and worship him who lives forever and ever. They cast their crowns before the throne..."
Revelation 4:10 (ESV)

Donkey

The donkey is seen on the side of the road,
with **LARGE**, heavy bundles, she carries her load.
The foal of a donkey, a yearling at best,
gave Jesus a place for His body to rest.
As He rode into town, loud *hosannas* did ring,
that triumphal entry marked Jesus as KING.

"And Jesus found a young donkey and sat on it, just as it is written."
John 12:14 (NIV)

Flocks and Herds

The hillsides were filled with animals that night.

They were present and saw when there shone a great light.

The shepherds, along with their flocks and their herd,

were some of the first to receive the good word,

that **GOD'S** only Son had been born on that day.

He came to redeem us and show us the way.

"The next day he saw Jesus coming toward him, and said, 'Behold, the Lamb of God, who takes away the sin of the world!'"
John 1:29 (ESV)

Fox

The **SLY** red fox is a beautiful creature.

The way that he hunts is a well-known feature.

He *prowls* in the night when the lighting is dim.

He does it this way, so others won't see him.

The fox uses **DARKNESS** as part of his fight.

But God prefers people to walk in His light.

"Very truly I tell you, whoever believes in me will do the works I have been doing, and they will do even greater things than these, because I am going to the Father."
John 14:12 (NIV)

Lion

The lion is king and commands by his **ROAR**.

His pride is protected from threats at their door.

The male is fierce, but he puts on a big front,

for it is the *female* that goes out to hunt.

She sneaks up and waits for a chance at her prey.

God says our enemy hunts in the same way.

"Be alert and of sober mind. Your enemy the devil prowls around like a roaring lion looking for someone to devour."
1 Peter 5:8 (NIV)

Mouse

Too many people are afraid of a mouse,
especially when seen inside of their house.
The thing to remember, a fact that is true,
that a very small mouse is more fearful of **you**.
We should remain calm if a mouse should appear,
for God does not give us the spirit of *fear*.

"...for God gave us a spirit not of fear but of power and love and self-control."
2 Timothy 1:7 (ESV)

Otter

Otters are *playful* and they like to have fun.

They swim in the water and bask in the sun.

Their home is a burrow, a good place to hide.

The path to their doorway is more like a slide.

It's great to be *playful* for each girl and boy.

But living for Jesus brings Him so much **joy**.

"Sing to him a new song;
play skillfully, and shout for joy."
Psalm 33:3 (NIV)

Oxen

A team of oxen, to have value and worth,

must be yoked together soon after their birth.

They both think as **ONE** and the work they do share,

because all that they do must be done as a pair.

The will of the Father and not of our own,

allows us to serve **HIM** who sits on the throne.

"Do not be yoked together with unbelievers. For what do righteousness and wickedness have in common? Or what fellowship can light have with darkness?"
2 Corinthians 6:14 (NIV)

Sheep

The cute-factor's high in each newborn lamb,

it doesn't much matter whether ewe or ram.

Sheep stay together while the shepherd stands guard,

for the life of a lamb on their own would be hard.

So much like sheep, we can wander and stray,

but Jesus, our Shepherd, will show us the way.

"...but God shows his love for us in that while we were still sinners, Christ died for us."
Romans 5:8 (ESV)

Zebra

The colors on each zebra are quite a sight.

Are they WHITE on **BLACK** or maybe **BLACK** on WHITE?

The stripes on their body help them blend and hide.

They look like a horse but are harder to ride.

People see the outside as a work of art,

But God sees our *beauty* from what's in our HEART.

"For the LORD sees not as man sees: man looks on the outward appearance,
but the LORD looks on the heart."
1 Samuel 16:7 (ESV)

Animals that differ with *fur*, *fin*, or *feather*,
have learned how to live alongside of each other.
Their **habits**, their **food**, their **homes** aren't the same,
yet God knows each one and He calls them by name.

Each turtle that hatches and crawls to the sea,
each colt that is born to run wild and free,
all come to exist in the air, sea, and land,
by God's **MIGHTY** power and His *loving* hand.

Yet we are **unique**, quite different, and odd,
because we are created in the *image* of God.

"So God created mankind in his own image.
in the image of God he created them;
male and female he created them."
Genesis 1:27 (NIV)

Ben grew up on a family farm in Western Pennsylvania and has been around animals all of his life. He graduated from Penn State University with an Agricultural Science degree and worked over 30 years with the Maryland Department of Agriculture as an Ag Specialist. Ben graduated from the Cornerstone Bible Institute in 1996. He also teaches beekeeping classes at a local college and mentors his students from those classes.

BEN COOPER
AUTHOR

He is an award-winning author and enjoys speaking about God's marvelous creative works, particularly how observing the plants and animals gives testimony that we are fearfully and wonderfully made by a loving God.

Ben serves his local church in camping ministries and has been on several short-term mission trips outside of the U.S. He and his wife have five adult children who were all home schooled. They reside in the mountainous region of Southern Pennsylvania where he writes and enjoys working with his bees.

SANDY ARNOLD
ILLUSTRATOR

Sandy Arnold earned her BFA and Masters in Education, Special Education, from Frostburg State University. She currently teaches Fine Arts at Fort Hill High School in Cumberland, MD. Sandy also enjoys making soap and doing hive inspections in her apiary.

Painting has always been a meditative process for Sandy. It allows her to quietly reflect on the most important aspects of her life and honor them by creating a piece of artwork. Growing up in a rural town in West Virginia allowed for quiet exploration of all things flora and fauna. Walking barefoot through her father's vegetable garden, with the Appalachian Mountains as a backdrop, was a daily habit during the warm months. It was this upbringing that instilled a deep appreciation for all things grown and made by loving hands. Sandy would like to dedicate her artwork to her father who fostered her love of wildlife.

CPSIA information can be obtained
at www.ICGtesting.com
Printed in the USA
BVHW091330231121
622335BV00013B/382